Imagitronics

*Mind-Stretching Scenarios
to Launch Creative Thought and
Develop Problem-Solving Skills*

DON AMBROSE

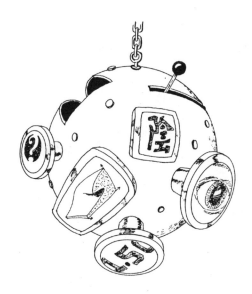

Zephyr Press

Tucson, Arizona

Imagitronics: Mind-Stretching Scenarios to Launch Creative Thought and Develop
Problem-Solving Skills
Grades 4–10

© 2002 by Don Ambrose

Printed in the United States of America

ISBN: 1-56976-141-8

Editing: Jenny Flynn
Design & Production: Dan Miedaner
Illustrations: Don Ambrose
Cover: Dan Miedaner

Published by:
Zephyr Press
P.O. Box 66006
Tucson, Arizona 85728-6006
800-232-2187
www://zephyrpress.com
www://i-home-school.com

Library of Congress Cataloging-in-Publication Data

Ambrose, Don, 1950-
    Imagitronics : mind-stretching scenarios to launch creative thought and develop
    problem-solving skills / Don Ambrose.
        p. cm.
    ISBN 1-56976-141-8 (pbk.)
        1. Creative thinking—Study and teaching—Activity programs.
    2. Critical thinking—Study and teaching—Activity programs. 3.
    Creation (Literary, artistic, etc.) I. Title.

    LB1590.5 .A42 2001
    370.15'2—dc21

                                                                        2001024065

Contents

Introduction

*"What if one were to run after a beam of light? . . .
What if one were riding on the beam?"*

—Albert Einstein

explaining his thought process when he formulated the special theory of relativity

Inspiring Creative, Critical, and Visual-Artistic Thought

Many of the world's greatest geniuses employ highly original visual
thought processes to generate their most profound achievements.
Einstein's visual-metaphorical thought experiments are classic
examples. On a lesser scale, everyday creativity often requires similar
imaginative insight. This book provides opportunities for children
and adults to invent and problem solve by confronting puzzling
scenarios that invite visual imagination.

The activities in this book are bite-size morsels that invite readers
to open their highly potent minds and to exercise their latent
imaginations. Each entry begins with a scenario that promotes
speculative imagination. The reader is invited to imagine the scenario
as real, to think critically, and to brainstorm solutions to problems or
ideas for inventions. In the creative- and critical-thinking section of
each entry, the reader is asked to approach the scenario from unusual
perspectives that promote creative insights and provide opportunities
for clever analysis and evaluation.

In the artistic design section, the reader is invited to employ
visual imagination once again: this time to create sketches of solutions
and invention designs. Those reluctant to do the artistic design (for
perceived lack of talent) are encouraged to do the designing anyway.
Refined art is not the primary objective. Imagination development is.
Some of our greatest imaginative thinkers use "stick-person" sketches
to capture their creative insights.

The reader will notice that the scenarios are accompanied by unusual drawings. These provide examples of what one can do with visual speculation, but they do not depict scenes from specific scenarios in order not to limit the imaginations of students.

The scenarios are clustered into sections by theme. Part 1, Science and Science Fiction Adventure, provides a variety of activities based on science concepts and science fiction topics. Part 2, Technological Innovation, includes technology-based scenarios that encourage inventive thought. In part 3, Social Studies—Imaginative Archaeology and Anthropology, imaginary archaeological discoveries and anthropological encounters with unusual, fictive cultures provide springboards for creative and critical thought about social issues and ethics. Finally, scenarios in part 4, Creative Architecture, engage the reader in architectural design.

Some Uses for the Book

Many scenarios can extend or enrich learning experiences in the science, social studies, arts, and language arts curricula.

- Each scenario with accompanying activities can serve as an activity card in an enrichment learning center or interest center.
- Selected scenarios can become the basis for, or extensions of, independent-study projects.
- Many of the scenarios can initiate whole-class, small-group, or individual creative writing activities.
- All of the scenarios initiate artistic design activities.
- Most of the scenarios can initiate or augment creative problem solving activities.
- The scenarios support curriculum integration by naturally incorporating artistic work in science, social studies, and language arts enrichment.

PART I

Science and Science Fiction

ADVENTURE

The growth of the human mind is still high adventure, in many ways the highest adventure on earth.

—Norman Cousins

SCIENCE AND
SCIENCE FICTION
ADVENTURE

1

Transgenic Additions to Humanity

Genetic engineers have been experimenting with the creation of new species by combining genetic information from different animal species (transgenesis). For instance, one of the earliest of these attempts resulted in a cross between a goat and a sheep. Imagine that transgenic experimentation gets out of hand and produces human-animal crosses such as rhinoman, lionwoman, waspman, and kangawoman. These transgenic humans remain mostly human but have some characteristics of the specified animal.

Creative and Critical Thinking

- What problems could such experimentation cause? Could anything good come from the creation of transgenic humans?

- Assume that these new transgenic humans are effectively assimilated into society. Also assume that some of them make the Olympic teams in their respective countries. In what sports would each of the previously mentioned transgenic humans excel? In what sports would they be at a disadvantage?

Artistic Design

- Draw rhinoman, lionwoman, waspman, and kangawoman. Also, make up an additional transgenic human and draw him or her.

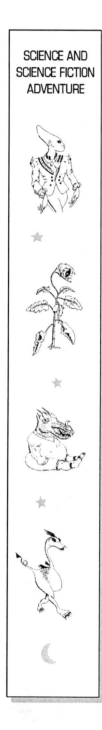

SCIENCE AND
SCIENCE FICTION
ADVENTURE

2

More Wacky Evolution

After accidentally traveling through a time warp, you find yourself propelled a million years into the future. Your major discovery is that genetic engineering in the 21st century caused some unusually rapid and strange developments in animal evolution. More specifically, it produced some strange cross-species combinations. Examples of these combinations include the following: mosquitolion, snakehorse, toadhog, lizarddog.

Creative and Critical Thinking

● If you had to have one of these animals as a pet, which would you pick? Why?

● Some scientists (the optimists) say that genetic engineering could do marvelous things for us, such as curing cancer and producing high-yield, drought- and pest-resistant crops. Others (the pessimists) warn that genetic engineering could cause serious environmental problems and create moral problems for which we are not prepared. Which group is right? Could both the optimists and the pessimists be partially right? Do some research on genetic engineering to find some answers to these questions.

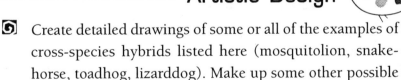

Artistic Design

⬡ Create detailed drawings of some or all of the examples of cross-species hybrids listed here (mosquitolion, snake-horse, toadhog, lizarddog). Make up some other possible examples and draw them.

3

Global Warming

Many scientists agree that our planet is heating up. It is possible that the heating could melt much of the glacial ice in the Arctic regions, thus raising the ocean levels and flooding coastal areas around the world. Many of the world's largest cities are seaports on or near the ocean, so places such as New York City, Seattle, London, Vancouver, and Tokyo could suffer from flooding that would make millions homeless, cause disease outbreaks, and destroy billions of dollars worth of property.

Creative and Critical Thinking

● What are some ways that coastal cities could be protected from rising ocean levels? Select your best solution and make it into a detailed plan.

● Pollution, such as car and truck exhaust, contributes to the problem of global warming. Nevertheless, people still buy large, gas-guzzling vehicles. How can they be convinced that their actions may be creating a serious problem that will hurt them later?

● How could you convince millions of people to move inland or to higher ground to avoid future coastal flooding when there seems to be no immediate danger?

Artistic Design

▣ Draw diagrams showing the details of your flood-protection plan. If you can, also make a clay or plaster model of your plan.

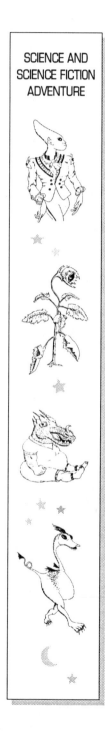

SCIENCE AND
SCIENCE FICTION
ADVENTURE

4

Expedition to Manta-Alpha

You are part of an interplanetary expedition exploring a small, warm planet called Manta-Alpha. The planet is mostly covered with water. You are standing on a mountaintop on one of the few small islands that dot the planet. The islands are very high, steep, and rocky. They are covered with jungle made up of tall, strange-looking, broad-leaved trees. The ocean is green and the sky yellow, with thick, dark clouds. The violent weather often includes powerful thunderstorms, lightning, and tornadoes.

I am a child playing on the seashore of knowledge.
—Sir Isaac Newton

Creative and Critical Thinking

- What kind of animal life would you find on this planet?

- If humanoids existed on this planet, what would they look like? What skills would they have developed?

Artistic Design

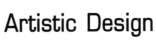 Draw the scene from your viewpoint at the top of the island. Draw a detailed close-up of a tree on the island.

SCIENCE AND
SCIENCE FICTION
ADVENTURE

5
Shrinking Syrup

A friend who is an amateur chemist created a potion in his basement. His intent was to create a drink that would enhance memory and thinking ability. Not being brave enough to try the potion himself, he convinced you to drink some. At first, the thick, sweet syrup seemed to do nothing, but eventually it caused you to shrink. Three days ago, you were as tall as a coffee table. Yesterday, you were as tall as a pen is long. Today, you are the size of a paper clip. Last night the cat chased you out into the vegetable garden. There is no way to tell if the shrinking will continue or if it will stop at some point. So far, the rate at which you are shrinking has been steady.

Creative and Critical Thinking

- What would be the most interesting thing about your shrinking experience?

- List five everyday items that would help you survive at your current paper-clip size. How would you use these items?

- What would it be like if the shrinking didn't stop? Do some research to find out what to expect when you shrink to a cellular, then molecular, then atomic, then subatomic size.

Artistic Design

 Sketch what you see in the garden from your level. Sketch what you might see two days from now.

SCIENCE AND
SCIENCE FICTION
ADVENTURE

6

Space Gardener

Y ou are the gardener in the greenhouse compartment of the CAGE Skymaster space station orbiting Earth in the year 2063. Your primary assignment is to develop vegetables that will feed the 2,400 technicians and scientists who live permanently on the station. Your greatest success so far is a fast-growing vine-like vegetable that can grow as tall as a two-story house. The vines are as thick as your arm and are covered with shiny, scaly, blue skin. The leaves are very long, twisted, irregular, and colorful. The plant produces several different kinds of very large, edible pods, seeds, and fruits. A single plant can provide 70% of the year-round nutritional needs for 50 people.

Creative and Critical Thinking

- Some of the scientists on board the station do research on your plant. They find that it immunizes humans against all known diseases but also shortens their life span by eight years. Consequently, people who regularly eat the products of the plant will live healthier but shorter lives. Would you eat food made from this plant? Why or why not?

- A visitor to the station takes some of the seeds back to Earth and plants them in a field. Your plant reproduces rapidly and uncontrollably, spreading across North America. What are the advantages and disadvantages of this unexpected course of events?

Artistic Design

- Draw your new vegetable and label its parts. Show cutaway views of the pods and seeds.

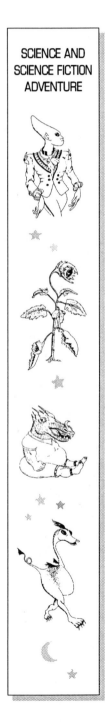

SCIENCE AND
SCIENCE FICTION
ADVENTURE

7

Birdpeople of Hawker

The planet Hawker is covered with evergreen forests and lakes. It is populated by birdpeople who are our size and look something like us except they have hooked beaks on their faces instead of noses. Feathers grow from their heads and arms. Their legs are very thin and they have birds' feet, with three toes and claws on each foot. The birdpeople can't take off and fly, but they can glide through the air for very long distances.

Imagination is more important than knowledge.
—Albert Einstein

Creative and Critical Thinking

- Imagine that you eat a mushroom from a Hawker forest, which transforms you into a birdperson for a month. What would be the advantages and disadvantages of being a birdperson?

- Write a short story describing your adventures during this interesting month.

Artistic Design

🌀 Draw a birdman or woman and sketch the inside of his or her house.

SCIENCE AND
SCIENCE FICTION
ADVENTURE

8

Munracks of Veltzar

On the planet Veltzar there is a race of humanoids called Munracks. The average Munrack is eight feet tall and has huge muscles and gray skin. It is hairless and has large red eyes with bright blue pupils; its ears are long and pointed. Most Munracks wear blue uniforms decorated with thick, flexible metal plates and belts. They never sleep except once a year, when all Munracks hibernate for about three weeks. Finally, nobody has ever seen a Munrack walk. They seem to run everywhere they go.

Creative and Critical Thinking

● Would you be able to live among the Munracks? What would be the most difficult adjustments you would have to make?

● On a visit to Veltzar you discover and translate a Munrackian history book. What does the book tell you about Munrackian history and culture? Think about their important historical events, beliefs, and holidays or festivals.

Artistic Design

▣ Draw a Munrack in what you think would be a typical Munrackian home.

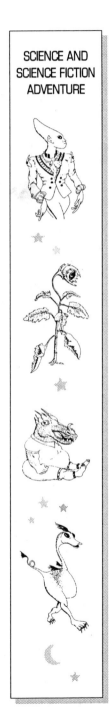

9

Robot Servant

In the year 2318, your new MR118 Blobbo robot is doing several household chores while serving you a cold drink. The robot is shaped like a large barrel with a green-tinted glass dome on top. Long, flexible antennae telescope in and out of small holes in this dome. The robot has three arms. One arm is long and flexible, with pinchers on the end. Another is short and has two six-fingered hands. The third arm has several attachments including magnets, brushes, and hoses. There are lights and buttons all over the body of the robot.

 Creative and Critical Thinking

- List all the possible uses for the robot. Select the most unusual of these uses and write about how these functions might change society.

- What might be some unforeseen problems with owning such a robot?

Artistic Design

- Draw a design of the robot and label all of its components.

SCIENCE AND
SCIENCE FICTION
ADVENTURE

10
Future City

After awakening from 200 years of frozen sleep in an underground cryogenics laboratory, you return to the surface to find your community transformed. It is now an enormous city consisting of huge buildings up to a mile in height. The buildings are strangely shaped and luminous, each radiating its own unique colors. There are no streets or traffic. In order to travel, people simply step into glass enclosures and instantly teleport to any location around the world. You also notice that the weather is under human control. In the daytime it is always sunny and 76 degrees Fahrenheit. At 8:30 in the evening, the sun goes down, and the temperature quickly changes to 68 degrees Fahrenheit. Wind and clouds are noticeably absent.

Creative and Critical Thinking

- If scientists are able to perfect cryogenic suspended animation, will that be a good thing? What would be the benefits and drawbacks?

- Living in a perfectly controlled climate sounds comfortable. Is there anything you would dislike about it?

- Write a short story about your experiences in this future city.

Artistic Design

- Draw what you see when you emerge from the underground lab. Also draw the interior of one of the buildings.

11

Dino Encounter

A time warp deposits you 145 million years in the past, in the Jurassic period. A dinosaur that we in the 21st century didn't know existed chases you into a cave. This dinosaur is 37 feet tall, and has a wrinkly hide and sharp teeth, which are each one foot long. It walks on huge hind legs, and its smaller front legs look like they were designed for digging. The creature has several bony spikes on its head and several more spikes on the end of its long, muscular tail. Its face is very long, with unusually large eyes for a dinosaur. It also has a long forked tongue.

Creative and Critical Thinking

● Make a list of everyday items from your home that you would like to take along with you to the Jurassic period to help you survive. Explain how you would use each item.

● Which of these items would be most valuable and why?

Artistic Design

Draw this dinosaur in side view, and sketch some close-up views of its face and front legs. Also, make a clay sculpture of the dinosaur's head.

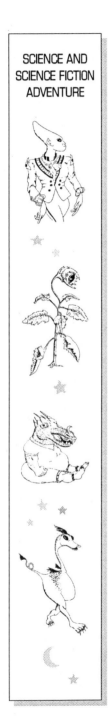

12
Dangerous Animal

Your close friend Onandega is captain of a scientific exploratory team visiting the planet Elphazeen. You are monitoring the work of the team from a base in another solar system. While walking on a path between the spectacular Dromada Twin Falls, one of Elphazeen's most famous landmarks, Onandega encounters a dangerous-looking animal. Onandega only has time to type six words to describe the animal into her wrist-messenger keypad before interstellar radiation blocks the signal. You are able to download only four of these words: leafy, hover, slug, and rotational.

Creative and Critical Thinking

- What could we learn from this animal? Speculate about its lifestyle and behavior patterns.

- What might the other two descriptive words have been? How would the addition of two more words change your speculations about the animal's appearance or behavior?

- What would you do in this situation if you were Onandega?

Artistic Design

🎨 Draw the animal that Onandega encountered.

SCIENCE AND
SCIENCE FICTION
ADVENTURE

13

Seacoast Visitor

O n the seashore, you see a strange little woman sitting on a boulder. She wears a long green cloak with a hood that covers her face. The cloak has interesting silver and blue designs and symbols printed on the back and sleeves. Seals and gulls are collecting in large numbers on the rocks around the woman. She is holding a device that occasionally emits very strange but beautiful sounds. Her legs are not really legs at all, but long, luminous tubes that stretch offshore and down into the ocean. The water is perfectly calm near her location, even though everywhere else up and down the shore, waves are crashing.

Creative and Critical Thinking

- Who is this woman and where is she from? List all the possibilities you can imagine.

- What is the purpose of the device she is holding?

Artistic Design

🌀 Draw this scene. Also draw an image of the woman's home as you imagine it.

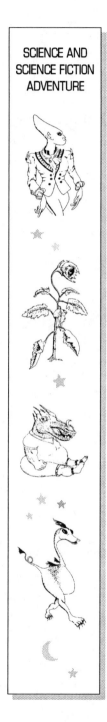

SCIENCE AND
SCIENCE FICTION
ADVENTURE

14

Prediction
Portal

A brilliant scientist, who happens to be a friend of yours, has invented a prediction portal through which you can catch momentary glimpses of possible futures. The portal scans future times and randomly settles on particular times for just a few minutes. After selecting a time, it shows a brief video of the landscape and everyday life while providing a readout of environmental information, such as levels of temperature, humidity, and pollutants. While you and your friend are giving the portal a test run, it settles on a time about a million years from now and gives you a look at two different possible futures. In one future, the temperature is quite cold in summer (just above freezing) and the humidity is very low. The pollution levels are also very low. In the other future, the temperature is very high (105 degrees Fahrenheit), as is the humidity (very damp, almost raining). Also, air pollution levels are high.

Creative and Critical Thinking

● How will humans of the future, and the descendants of your pet dog, have to adapt or evolve to fit into each of these future environments?

● If you had to spend the rest of your life in one of these environments, which one would you choose? Why?

Artistic Design

🎨 Draw some of the plants you might see in each future environment. Show cutaway views of the plants and label their parts.

SCIENCE AND
SCIENCE FICTION
ADVENTURE

15

Chaak, the Ice World

The planet Chaak is covered with a layer of ice that varies in depth from two to 65 miles. The temperature ranges from just below freezing in the warm season at the equator to 140 degrees below zero (Fahrenheit) at the poles. In addition, the wind constantly blows at high speeds across the entire surface of the planet. In spite of the conditions, the Urniks (the people of Chaak) have built large, modern cities using their only building material—ice. Many of the Urnik buildings have tall pillars, transparent domes, and slick ice slides for travel to adjacent buildings.

Creative and Critical Thinking

- How could the Urniks survive and thrive in such a formidable environment? Where would they get their energy and food?

- What methods would the Urniks use to build their impressive cities?

- What sports or other recreational activities would the Urniks invent?

Artistic Design

⟳ Draw the skyline of an Urnik city. Also draw the interior of a typical Urnik home.

SCIENCE AND
SCIENCE FICTION
ADVENTURE

16
Terran Gargantuan Space Station

You have returned from a two-month deep space mission aboard your Cyclops 217 exploratory runabout. Your craft is about to dock at Terran Gargantuan, a space station orbiting Earth. The station is huge, about ten miles long and three miles wide. It is made of five big titanium-steel globes with hundreds of windows and portholes in each. The globes have antennae, communication dishes, and solar panels attached to them. The five globes are connected by big metal beams and glass transportation tubes.

Creative and Critical Thinking

- What would be the qualifications of a good space station commander?

- What are all the possible purposes of the space station?

- How would you improve the design of the space station? Base your improvements on the three best purposes you thought of when answering the last question.

Artistic Design

- Draw the space station. Sketch a cutaway, cross-sectional view showing the inside of one of the station's five globes. Also, design your Cyclops 217 exploratory runabout.

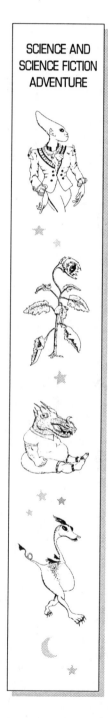

SCIENCE AND
SCIENCE FICTION
ADVENTURE

17

The Lost Expedition and the Survival Bus

You are on the planet Cerellus. Your expeditionary team consists of five explorers including yourself. Your mission is to find a lost group of explorers who disappeared on a previous mission, and it could take up to a year to find them. You need a "survival bus" in which to live and travel. The bus should carry enough food, water, and fuel to last a year. The weather on Cerellus is very hot, dry, and windy during the day and below freezing at night. It never rains, so the planet is bone dry. The landscape is rugged, covered with tall, jagged mountains and deep canyons. Some sandy deserts with huge dunes separate the mountain ranges. Except for the sandy deserts, the ground in most places is covered with large, sharp-edged rocks.

Creative and Critical Thinking

- How would you plan the search for the missing explorers?

- If you found life on Cerellus, what would it be like?

Artistic Design

⟳ Design the survival bus. Draw a diagram of it from the outside and a cutaway view showing the inside. Label the drawings. Also draw a landscape showing a typical scene on the surface of the planet.

SCIENCE AND
SCIENCE FICTION
ADVENTURE

18
Intelligent Trees

The planet Skuvian is inhabited by two species of conscious, intelligent trees. The tendril trees are light orange and very tall with thin trunks and many flexible vine-like branches. Instead of leaves, these branches are covered with a very fine wool-like substance. The bordeck trees are short with rough, dark purple bark. They have few leaves and branches.

Imagination is only intelligence having fun.
—George Scialabbe

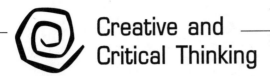

Creative and Critical Thinking

- A team of scientists has learned that these trees communicate with each other, even between species. What could be the possible topics of their communication?

- The trees don't have vocal cords, so how do they communicate?

- If we learned how to communicate with these trees, what could we learn from them? What could we teach them?

Artistic Design

- Sketch these trees in their natural environment.

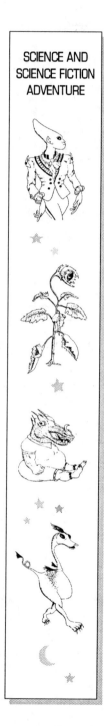

SCIENCE AND
SCIENCE FICTION
ADVENTURE

19
Air Chariots

You travel 100 years into the future to discover that everyone travels by air chariot. These are plastic platforms on which the driver and one or two passengers stand. The driver controls the chariot by twisting a set of handlebars and by using a touch pad on a small dashboard that rises up out of the platform. The chariot runs on magnetism and seems to have no engine. Lights on the base of the platform are used for communication with other drivers. Air chariots travel at a maximum height of 200 feet and a maximum speed of 70 miles per hour.

Creative and Critical Thinking

● What rules would air chariot drivers have to follow?

● What would you like or dislike about driving an air chariot?

● How would the invention of these chariots have changed the world?

Artistic Design

Design the blueprint for an air chariot and label its parts.

PART II

Technological
INNOVATION

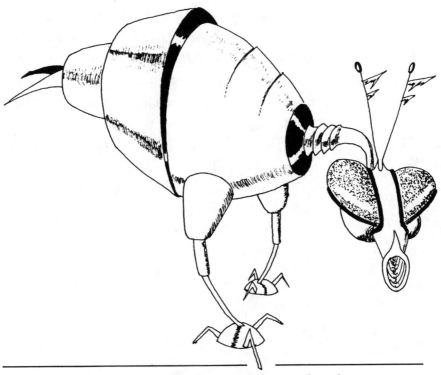

It is the great triumph of genius to make the common appear novel.

—J. W. Goethe

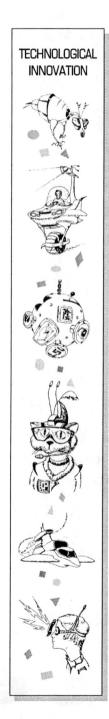

TECHNOLOGICAL
INNOVATION

20
Perfecto-Helmet

Concussions in hockey and football games seem to be on the rise. Today's players are bigger and stronger; consequently, injuries are becoming more serious. You have been assigned the task of bringing together a helmet-improvement task force. Design either a hockey or a football helmet that will provide perfect protection and be so light and comfortable that a player will hardly notice he or she is wearing it. If possible, borrow real helmets to analyze their construction and materials. Use this analysis to help you with the design.

Creative and Critical Thinking

- What professionals would you recruit for the task force? (Whose expertise would you need?)
- In addition to improving the helmet, what other steps could be taken to reduce head injuries in the sport you selected?
- What other uses might there be, outside the game, for your new helmet?

Artistic Design

- Draw a design for the new helmet. Show both side and front views, as well as a cutaway view showing the materials and construction. Label the parts.

TECHNOLOGICAL
INNOVATION

21
Pufferblock

You have just finished the plans for a device that will prevent children and adolescents from starting smoking. The device is small and wearable as a decorative article of clothing. It looks so good that it could become a status symbol for those who wear it, thus giving it high potential as a widespread deterrent for smoking.

What we want is to see the child in pursuit of knowledge and not knowledge in pursuit of the child.
—George Bernard Shaw

Creative and Critical Thinking

- How does the device work? Does it have or need a power supply? What are its component materials?
- Aside from your device, are there other ways to prevent children and adolescents from smoking?
- What problems might you face in your attempts to popularize and market your anti-smoking device? How would you address these problems?

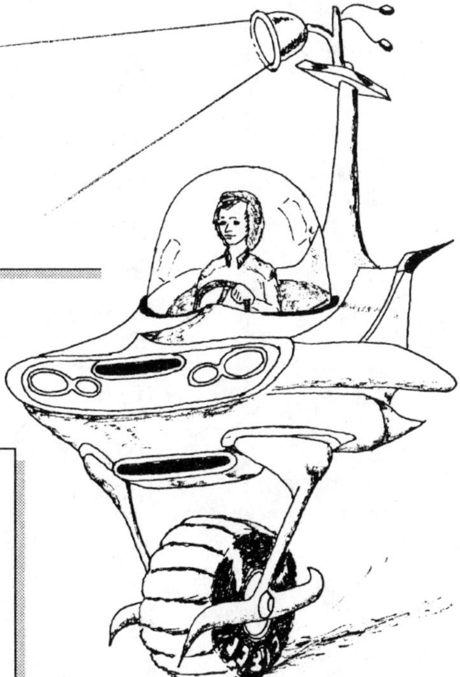

Artistic Design

- Draw a design for the device. Label it to show how it works. Also, create a magazine advertisement or a one-minute video ad that will make both parents and children want to buy the device.

22
Survival Knife

Most wilderness adventurers carry a survival knife in case they are stranded for long periods without food or shelter. A survival knife is usually quite large and is kept in a leather holder. One side of the blade is very sharp and the other is generally serrated (saw-toothed). Some survival knives have hollow handles for storage of matches. Some even have a compass embedded in the end of the handle. These knives are made to serve a wide variety of purposes, including repair, shelter building, and food preparation.

Can you design a new, improved survival knife? It should be able to stay sharp for years; saw down small trees; stitch clothing; hammer tent pegs; telescope into a short sword; fillet fish; signal aircraft during the day by reflection and at night by firing flares; start fires; pick up and send radio messages; help guide you through the wilderness; and store maps. Think of three other uses for the knife and work those uses into your design.

Creative and Critical Thinking

▶ Write up a step-by-step plan for survival in the woods based on the use of your knife.

▶ If you were lost in a remote forest, and you had just one other item besides the knife, what would that item be? What are the reasons for your choice?

Artistic Design

✗ Draw the design for your new, improved survival knife. Label its parts and, where necessary, explain how they work.

23

Music
Blaster

Y ou are the manager of a rock group that uses a new kind of musical instrument. It is a combination percussion, wind, string, and electric noisemaker. The sound arises from a combination of electricity, forced air, and colliding and scraping parts within its casing. The instrument is so large that it takes three people to carry it and a midsize truck to haul it from one city to the next. There are electronic touch pads, dials, buttons, and levers all over it. In order to use the instrument, two stage-hands have to bolt it in place on the stage so two musicians can safely play it.

Creative and Critical Thinking

- How might the invention of the music blaster change the music industry?
- What ideas from existing musical instruments or other objects could you combine to create another, different sort of music blaster? Try combining some of the following: drums, foghorn from a ship, electric sander, trumpet, piano.

Artistic Design

- Design the music blaster. Label its parts, showing the purpose of each electronic touch pad, dial, button, and lever. Show the two musicians playing it. Also, make a sculpture or model of the instrument, if you can.

TECHNOLOGICAL
INNOVATION

24
Spy Pen

An international intelligence agency needs a ballpoint pen that can do the following: write; take pictures; help a spy see in the dark; throw a smoke screen; put enemy agents to sleep; signal and download information from a global-positioning satellite (tells you where you are on the planet); and burn through a thin steel cable.

Creative and Critical Thinking

▶ The spy business slowed down after the Soviet Union collapsed. Consequently, the government was left with 5,000 useless spy pens, and you bought them at an auction. You want to sell the pens at a profit, but first you need to convince people of their value. Brainstorm all the possible uses for the spy pen.

▶ Pick the three or four best uses for the pens and write an advertising jingle (a catchy little song) that will sell your pens on radio advertisements. Design a magazine advertisement to sell your pens. Produce a 30-second video commercial to sell the pens.

Artistic Design

❀ Design the spy pen and label its parts, showing how they work. Include a cutaway drawing showing how the pen is constructed and the materials used.

TECHNOLOGICAL INNOVATION

25
A Surefire Cross-Country Winner

You have just bought a TXR7 Bohami, a cross-country racecar, for $3,750,000. It has two ramjet engines, a smoke-screen device, a removable top, radar, and an infrared scanner for night driving. Its six wheels, each with independent suspension, make the car capable of traveling over very rough terrain. Most of the time, however, you will want to stay on smooth, paved roads where you will be able to reach speeds of 280 miles per hour in five seconds.

Creative and Critical Thinking

▶ Can you make the car even better? If you can, explain your improvements in written form or by drawing a diagram.

▶ What would it be like if everyone had a TXR7 Bohami? How would the streets, highways, and traffic rules change?

Artistic Design

✖ Imagine sitting in the driver's seat. Draw the dashboard and interior of the car from your point of view. Also draw a side view of the car.

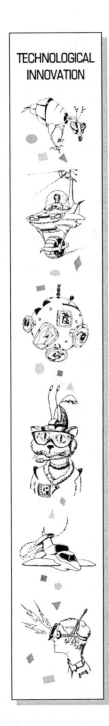

TECHNOLOGICAL
INNOVATION

26

The Ultimate Ride

Amusement-park rides seem to be getting bigger, faster, and more exciting. Are there ways to make them even more exciting without making them more dangerous? Think about the following characteristics and features of amusement-park rides: speed, height, rapid acceleration and deceleration, direction changes, spin, surprise, depth, decoration, noise, tracks, wheels, sleds, and capsules. Use some or all of these characteristics and features to design the ultimate amusement-park ride. Also consider combining aspects of different rides that you have seen or experienced.

The Ultimate Ride

Creative and Critical Thinking

▶ Analyze what you consider the most interesting amusement-park rides for the following: What makes them exciting? How safe are they? What improvements would you make on them (other than the improvements you included in your ultimate ride)?

▶ Use some of the following words to generate a few additional modifications to your design for the ultimate ride: slither, explode, separate, grind, hammer, and float.

Artistic Design

⚒ Draw the design for this ride. Label its parts and briefly describe how it works. Be sure to explain its safety features.

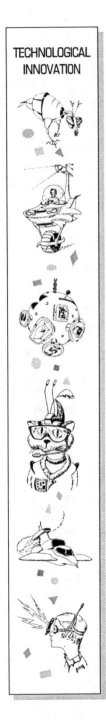

TECHNOLOGICAL
INNOVATION

27
Ugly
Insect

You are a scientist in the Amazon rain forest using a magnifying glass to study some leaves from a newly discovered jungle plant. As you focus on a particular cluster of leaves, the strangest, ugliest insect you have ever seen comes into view. The insect is so bizarre and ugly that you can hardly speak as you try to dictate a description into your recorder. All you can do is utter the following words: stringy, slimy, sharp, coiled, gritty, and spongy. You do manage to take a photo of the insect for *Discover* magazine.

Creative and Critical Thinking

▶ Some indigenous people in the Amazon tell you that the insect is magical. What could this statement mean? List all the possibilities.

▶ You work hard as a scientist, but on the weekends you are inventing a revolutionary new riding lawn mower that will do much more than just cut grass. Can you improve the design of your mower by borrowing design ideas from the structure of the new insect that you've just discovered?

Artistic Design

※ Draw the insect and label its parts. Alternatively, use materials such as wire, clay, or sponges to make a sculpture of the insect.

TECHNOLOGICAL
INNOVATION

28
Behemoth
Jet

An aircraft manufacturer has just built the largest passenger plane in the world. It is the length of four football fields and is the height of a 10-story building. It is more streamlined than any existing passenger plane. There are nine levels in the passenger compartment, and when fully loaded the plane will carry 12,000 passengers and 86 crew members. Eight enormous jet engines on each wing and three on the tail power the plane. Each of the 24 tires on the landing gear is too large to fit into a typical school classroom.

Visual imagery is usually essential for scientific advance.

—Arthur I. Miller

Creative and Critical Thinking

▶ What transportation problems would this new plane solve? What new problems might it create?

▶ Would a huge plane such as this actually be capable of flight? Do some research to find out.

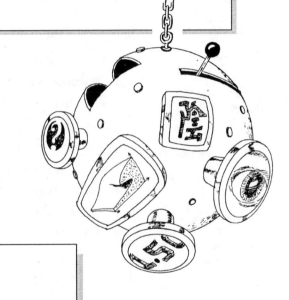

Artistic Design

✖ Draw a design of the plane, showing a side view and a cutaway view of the inside.

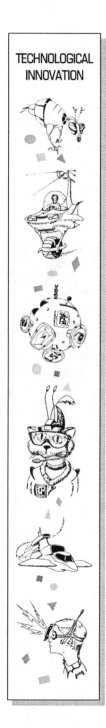

TECHNOLOGICAL
INNOVATION

29

Cycle-Copter

Your new invention is a jet-powered cycle-copter: a single-seat combination motorcycle and helicopter with a small jet engine. Its maximum speeds are 200 miles per hour on the ground and 500 miles per hour in the air. The vehicle has retractable chopper blades that extend somewhat behind the rear wheel when retracted. This feature provides some aerodynamic stability during road travel. When in the air, the windshield extends up and over the driver, providing a protective bubble.

Creative and Critical Thinking

▶ What would be the pros and cons of owning one of these cycle-copters?

▶ When the automobile became popular early in the 20th century, it brought about big changes in society. For example, huge highway systems were built, motels appeared, people traveled more, and pollution increased. If your cycle-copter became popular, how might it change our society?

Artistic Design

✖ Draw a design of the cycle-copter, complete with labels of its parts.

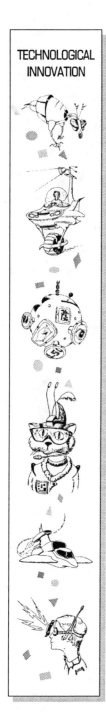

TECHNOLOGICAL
INNOVATION

30

Snow Cat Cargo Driver

You are driving a huge Snow Cat, a half-track cargo vehicle, from the seashore of Antarctica to a base at the South Pole. The vehicle has rubber wheels on the front and caterpillar tracks on the cargo compartment in the back. The front of the vehicle is small, with only a cabin for the driver. The cabin is, however, very comfortable. The cargo compartment is enormous: about the size of a large shopping mall. A swivel device joins the front and back sections.

Creative and Critical Thinking

▶ What might you be carrying to the base at the South Pole? Why would you need such a huge cargo vehicle to carry it?

▶ There is a small emergency kit under the seat in the cabin. What would you hope to find in the emergency kit if the vehicle broke down?

▶ Write an short adventure story about your expedition.

Artistic Design

✖ Draw a side view of the vehicle. Also draw the interior of the driver's cabin.

TECHNOLOGICAL
INNOVATION

31

Buried
Treasure

Y ou are a world-class engineer. A mysterious group of people has hired you for a peculiar task. The group wants you to bury on a tropical island a small sealed box of something very valuable. As members of the group prefer to remain anonymous, you meet with a go-between, who gives you written instructions for the burial. You are required to bury the box 200 feet deep and to create at least 10 traps and decoys to thwart anyone who might attempt to dig it up. Your plans must ensure that the box will remain buried for several centuries.

Creative and Critical Thinking

▶ Why is the box so valuable? List five things the box might contain. Select one item and explain why it is the most likely.

▶ Although the group will pay you very well for this project, you aren't sure you want to do it. Make a list of questions you want to ask the members of this mysterious group.

Artistic Design

※ Draw a diagram of your plans for the burial. Label and describe all the traps and decoys.

TECHNOLOGICAL INNOVATION

32

Bionic Vehicle

Inventors who employ the creative-thinking strategy of bionics use ideas from nature to generate inventions. After hearing about this strategy, you decide to use ideas from nature to invent a new car or truck. After a morning at the zoo, you come home with some promising ideas for models. You are especially inspired by an owl's eyes, an ostrich's legs, a lizard's body, a tiger's claws, and a bat's sonar. Using these ideas, you design and build a prototype of your vehicle.

Creative and Critical Thinking

▶ After creating your design for the vehicle (see design activity below), show it to a friend. Use his or her ideas to make at least one improvement to the vehicle.

▶ What are some uses for your new vehicle? Who would buy it?

Artistic Design

※ Draw a design for your vehicle, including a side view and a cutaway view of the inside. Label the important features of the vehicle.

TECHNOLOGICAL
INNOVATION

33

Insect Ideas for the Playground

Some children bore easily, even on the playground. On a sunny day in the park, you are watching children playing on the swings, monkey bars, slides, and merry-go-round. You are also getting bored, so your mind wanders to the nearby shrubs, grass, and puddles, where you observe the actions of grasshoppers, bees, ants, and water bugs. As a creative individual, you begin to apply the bionic creative-thinking strategy. You use design ideas from the insects to imagine improvements to the playground equipment in the park and to design entirely new playground equipment.

Creative and Critical Thinking

▶ Think carefully about your new playground equipment designs. Are there any aspects of the new designs that make them more dangerous than the old equipment? If so, how can you make them safer?

▶ Now let's think in reverse. Is there anything about the design of the old playground equipment that could improve the design of the insects?

Artistic Design

※ Draw the designs for your new pieces of playground equipment. Provide labels where necessary to show how they work.

TECHNOLOGICAL
INNOVATION

34

Quicksilver Skateboard

Skateboarding is a popular pastime that requires great skill and coordination. Skateboarders are always pushing the envelope, trying ever more dangerous stunts. Steep, paved mountain roads attract skateboarders because the roads provide long, smooth downhill stretches on which a skateboard can build up considerable speed. Design a skateboard that could handle high-speed (100 miles per hour) coasting down paved mountain roads. The skateboard should be capable of sharp turns at high speeds. It also should have an auxiliary power source for climbing hills, as well as an emergency brake.

Discovery is seeing what everybody has seen and thinking what nobody has thought.
—Albert Szent-Gyorgyi

Creative and
Critical Thinking

▶ Other than entertainment, what uses might people find for your skateboard?

▶ What problems might occur if your skateboard became popular?

▶ Invent an Olympic sport in which your new skateboard would play an important part.

Artistic
Design

✕ Draw a design for your new skateboard.

TECHNOLOGICAL
INNOVATION

35

Voyage to Proxima Centauri

Interstellar travel always has been beyond our capabilities, but that may change soon. The nearest star to our solar system is Proxima Centauri, which is 4.25 light-years away. Consequently, traveling there at the speed of light would take 4.25 years; traveling at half the speed of light would take almost nine years, and so on. Design a spacecraft that would keep you and four friends alive for at least the nine-year voyage (assuming that it can sustain half the speed of light for the duration of the trip). Of course, your craft must have sufficient living space and cargo space for supplies without the craft becoming too large and expensive.

Creative and Critical Thinking

▶ Make a list of essential items for this trip.

▶ What social or emotional problems might your crew of five face on such a trip? How could you plan ahead and prepare for these problems?

▶ Based on new discoveries in the sciences, NASA engineers are making plans for long-term space flight. Use the Internet and science magazines to research these plans. Present your findings to some friends or to a class in school.

Artistic Design

※ Draw and label a cross-sectional diagram of the ship, showing its engine room, cargo bays, living quarters, and any other design features you decide are necessary.

TECHNOLOGICAL
INNOVATION

36

Tireless Tires

As a NASA engineer, you have been assigned the task of designing tires for a dune buggy that will be used for exploration of Mars during an upcoming expedition. The tires must not blow out or deflate when traveling over sharp rocks. They should provide excellent traction on steep, smooth rock faces, and they must not sink in deep sand. In addition, they should provide superior shock absorption that will protect the sensitive scientific equipment in the buggy. As a final requirement, the leader of your engineering team wants you to create a way for the tires to serve as containers for the batteries that power the vehicle.

Creative and Critical Thinking

- After creating the tire design, use the words "cat" and "octopus" to generate ideas for additional modifications to your plan.
- What could be used in place of tires on the dune buggy?

Artistic Design

- Draw the design plan for the tires, complete with explanatory labels. Include a cutaway view showing the inside of the tires. Also, sketch the dune buggy traveling across the Martian surface.

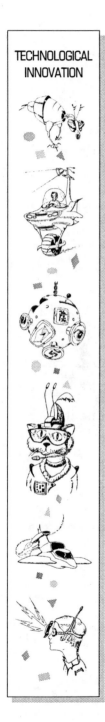

TECHNOLOGICAL
INNOVATION

37
Supersub

As a member of an oceanography team, you need a small research submarine that can navigate along the rough Pacific coastline of North America. It must travel through narrow inlets and cave entrances during rough storms, so it must be capable of precise and quick directional changes both on the surface and below. Its primary purpose is to take your team of three explorers into small, dark, irregular undersea caves where you can collect plant and rock samples. Some of these explorations will require the team to spend a week or more under the surface, so the sub will need living quarters.

Creative and Critical Thinking

▶ If you were to hire the other two members of your research team, what personality characteristics and skills should the new people have? Put the list items in order of priority from most important to least.

▶ Other than its original purpose (research), in what other ways could the submarine be put to use?

Artistic Design

※ Design the research submarine showing both a side view and a cutaway cross section that portrays the inside. Add a brief written description of what makes this submarine capable of precise maneuvering in tight spaces.

TECHNOLOGICAL
INNOVATION

38

Ingenious
Roller Skates

The construction and materials of roller skates have changed considerably over the years. People want skates that will enable them to move faster with more agility. They also want improved ankle support and comfort. What will roller skates be like 100 years from now? Create a plan for improved skates. Think about how to use new materials, improve comfort, streamline for speed, increase durability, and enhance decoration. Use the following words to give you additional design ideas for the new skates: slick, Velcro, explode, and magnet.

Through being creative we become creative.
—Howard Gruber

Creative and Critical Thinking

▶ Invent and explain a new game that could be played using these roller skates.

▶ For what other purposes could your new skates be used?

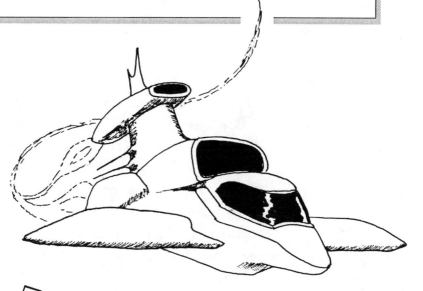

Artistic Design

※ Draw your plans for the new skates. Label the parts and materials.

TECHNOLOGICAL
INNOVATION

39
Multipurpose Power Tool

After helping with some home improvement projects, you are tired of running to fetch different tools. You decide to invent a multipurpose workshop power tool that will pound nails, drive screws, sand wood, sharpen knives, drill holes, and saw boards. It also has its own light source for working in dark corners. Finally, it precisely measures materials and vacuums sawdust as it works.

Creative and Critical Thinking

▶ Think of at least three more functions for the power tool that you might include without making it much more cumbersome than it already is.

▶ Make up an advertising jingle or a poster to market your invention.

Artistic Design

※ Draw a design for this tool. Illustrate it from a side, front, or top view and label the components, showing how they are put together.

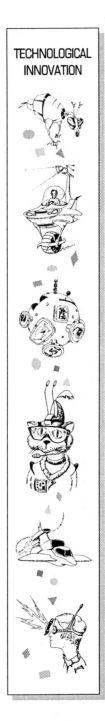

TECHNOLOGICAL
INNOVATION

40

30,000-
Foot Drop

As a member of a special rescue team, you must parachute into hostile territory to help someone escape from imprisonment by a dictator. The terrain into which you will descend is mountainous, so pinpoint navigation during your fall will be important. Unfortunately, the leader of your team has decided that a parachute drop is too dangerous because you will be visible for too long from the ground. You must jump from a plane flying at 30,000 feet—without a parachute or a hang glider, which would also keep you aloft too long. Your task now is to design equipment you can wear that will help you survive the fall.

Creative and Critical Thinking

▶ What design features could you build into your suit to help you navigate to the correct landing point during a high-speed fall into mountainous terrain?

▶ What design features would help you decelerate enough to survive the fall?

▶ Write a short story describing your experiences on this rescue mission.

▶ What other ways could you attempt to rescue the stranded person? Brainstorm strategies and rank them from best to worst.

Artistic Design

※ Draw yourself wearing your jumpsuit and survival equipment. Label the pieces of equipment and explain their functions.

TECHNOLOGICAL
INNOVATION

41

Adventure Game Boots

As part of an adventure vacation, you are preparing for a game in which you will be left alone for two weeks on an island off the Alaskan coast. The island is 10 miles long and two miles wide and the terrain is very steep and rocky. Most of the island is covered with evergreen trees. It is late autumn so days are cool and often rainy, while nights are cold and damp. According to the rules of the game, you are allowed to bring nothing but the following to the island: a light cotton T-shirt, cotton shorts, one pair of cotton socks, and a pair of survival boots that you can design yourself. The boots may be made of any material and their construction is entirely left to your imagination. Innovative boot design is part of the game.

Creative and Critical Thinking

▶ Given the challenges of your stay on the island, what should be the functions of your boots? What materials and design ideas would you use to meet these functions?

▶ Adventure vacations are becoming more popular. Brainstorm other promising ideas and locations for such vacations.

▶ What are the pros and cons of adventure vacations?

Artistic Design

※ Draw a design for your set of boots. Include a labeled cutaway view showing all of the details and materials.

TECHNOLOGICAL
INNOVATION

42
Lounge Chair

After a long, hard day you want to do nothing but relax. Unfortunately, your sofa and easy chair just don't feel right. Being an inventive person, you put your creative mind to work and soon come up with a design for the ultimate lounge chair. It is the most comfortable chair in the world. In addition, it provides everything you could possibly want during a relaxing evening at home.

Creative and Critical Thinking

▶ Use some of the following words to generate even more improvements for the chair you design: wave, fog, bird, and layers.

▶ It would be great to have such a chair; however, it could create some unanticipated problems. What might these problems be? How could you overcome them?

Artistic Design

✖ Draw a detailed blueprint for your chair. Label its design features and materials. Where necessary, explain how the special features work.

TECHNOLOGICAL
INNOVATION

43

Microplane

You have just finished building the prototype of the Sparrow: a new single-seat commuter aircraft. It is simply made so it will be affordable (about the cost of a full-size car or minivan) when you start to mass-produce it. The Sparrow will fit into a standard parking space after its small wings and tail fold up. In order to avoid the need for runways, you've designed it to take off vertically to about 100 feet before its wings unfold and it begins to fly toward a destination. It also can land vertically. Its top speed of 180 miles per hour and maximum range of 300 miles make it perfect for short commuting trips to and from work or shopping, but not very effective for long trips. With its wings and tail folded, the Sparrow also can travel on the highway like a car, but only at a maximum speed of 35 miles per hour.

Creative and Critical Thinking

▶ What things would a young person who just finished college have to consider before making the decision to buy or not to buy the Sparrow?

▶ What unforeseen benefits and problems could the Sparrow create for our society? Would it create the need for any new laws? If so, what would these laws be?

Artistic Design

※ Draw a side and front view of the Sparrow with wings and tail extended. Draw side and front views of the plane with wings and tail folded. Also draw a labeled cutaway side view showing the important parts of the plane.

TECHNOLOGICAL
INNOVATION

44

Comfort
Shoes

After a hard day's work, your feet are sore. It is time to invent the most comfortable shoes the world has ever seen. The Comfort Shoe should be soft and pliable, yet firm enough for support. These shoes should keep your feet cool in hot weather and warm in the cold while being waterproof but breathable. They should be very easy to put on and remove but must not slip off too easily. Their tread design should make them nonslip on any surface. Also, they should be so durable that they will last a lifetime. Finally, shoes this perfect will have to be expensive, so most people will only buy one pair. Consequently, the shoes should be capable of changing color to match any outfit.

Creative and
Critical Thinking

▶ Use some of the following words to generate more ideas for improvements to your shoes: parachute, penguin, bicycle, and turtle.

▶ Is it even possible to construct such perfect shoes? If not, why not? If it is possible, what materials and construction methods might be necessary?

Artistic Design

※ Draw the design plan for your Comfort Shoes. Include a cutaway view with labels for the materials and design features.

45

Speedboat

You are attempting to get into *The Guinness Book of World Records* by making the fastest trip by boat across the Atlantic Ocean. The speed you hope to achieve in the crossing is an average of 350 miles per hour. Your early boat-design plans include two jet engines, an auxiliary rocket engine, a plastic-bubble cockpit, searchlights, drag chutes, and special attention to aerodynamic streamlining. The ocean is several thousand miles across, so fuel could be a problem. In addition, the Atlantic is rough, so your boat will have to cope with strong winds and big, choppy waves.

Creative and Critical Thinking

- Is there anything wrong with the early design plans?
- Make a list of important problems, issues, and opportunities to consider in the planning and building of this boat. Adjust your design plans based on some of the points in this list.

Artistic Design

- Draw the design plans for the boat. Include a cutaway view showing its materials and construction details.

TECHNOLOGICAL
INNOVATION

46

Luxurious
Desk

Anyone who has gone to school knows that students' desks can be uncomfortable. Maybe everyone would learn more and get along better if the desks were improved. Can you design improvements to the typical student's desk that would make it more comfortable, efficient, and convenient? In addition, there always seems to be someone prone to committing vandalism, so the desk must be easy to clean and repair. If you can create a promising improvement plan, you might get to enjoy its benefits before you graduate!

Creative and Critical Thinking

▶ Brainstorm a list of all the needs and wants of students (comfortable seat, storage for books, snacks, privacy . . .). This list should give you some ideas for improvement.

▶ How can you make these improvements while keeping the costs of construction down? Do some research to find out which of your improvement ideas will cost the most, then make plans to trim the costs without completely losing the benefit of these ideas.

Artistic Design

※ Draw the design plan for your new desk. Label and describe the parts where necessary.

TECHNOLOGICAL INNOVATION

47

Harmless Riot Control

In our development as a species we are coming to the point at which we believe it is wrong to hurt people and animals unnecessarily. Consistent with this development, some law-enforcement agencies are looking for nonviolent ways to immobilize criminals and control rioting crowds. The rubber bullet is a crude example. As a highly creative thinker, you can do better. Can you invent a riot-control device that can keep hundreds of angry rioters at bay without hurting them?

My total conscious search in life has been for a new seeing, a new image, a new insight.
—Louise Nelson

Creative and Critical Thinking

▶ What are all the possible design options for this device? What materials could you use to construct it?

▶ Are there nonviolent ways to control angry mobs without using your new device? Think of some possible methods and select the best one. Write a brief description of how this method would work.

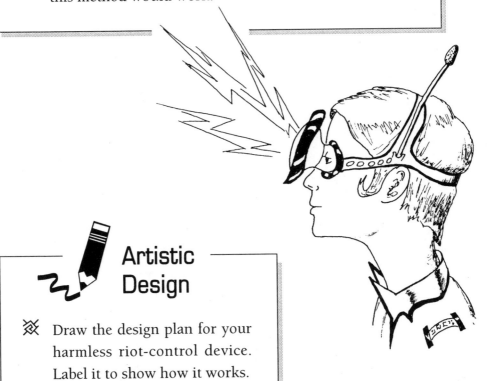

Artistic Design

✳ Draw the design plan for your harmless riot-control device. Label it to show how it works.

PART III

Social Studies

IMAGINATIVE ARCHAEOLOGY
AND
ANTHROPOLOGY

Obstacles are those frightful things you see when you take your eyes off the goal.

—Hannah Moore

SOCIAL STUDIES:
IMAGINATIVE
ARCHAEOLOGY
AND
ANTHROPOLOGY

48
Coexistence

You are an anthropologist visiting the Cyaneran people on the distant planet Ryboculum. The Cyanerans are kind, peaceful people who have developed an advanced culture. They live simply but comfortably, and their art and music are the most advanced you have ever encountered. The Cyanerans have neighbors, the Lysomians, who are aggressive and warlike. The Lysomians outnumber the Cyanerans ten to one. Surprisingly, in discussions with Cyaneran leaders you have found no evidence of conflict between the Cyanerans and Lysomians. It appears that they have lived peacefully side-by-side for at least 600 years. Other cultures exist on Ryboculum, but you have yet to learn about them.

We can easily forgive a child who is afraid of the dark. The real tragedy of life is when men are afraid of the light.

—Plato

Creative and Critical Thinking

■ Given their circumstances and characteristics, how could the Cyanerans and Lysomians coexist this long without conflict? Consider all possible explanations.

■ How would the governments of the Cyanerans and Lysomians differ?

Artistic Design

◰ Draw portraits of a Cyaneran and a Lysomian. Produce a Cyaneran painting or sculpture.

SOCIAL STUDIES:
IMAGINATIVE
ARCHAEOLOGY
AND
ANTHROPOLOGY

49

Deciphering a Coin

In an old treasure chest you discover a huge, solid gold coin the size of a dinner plate. An archaeologist tells you that the coin was made in an ancient civilization in central Africa, and that very little is known about the people who lived in that location at that time. A side view of a woman's head is engraved at the center of the coin. The image shows the woman wearing what appear to be large pieces of jewelry. Also engraved on the coin are eight pieces of innovatively designed furniture, which form a circle surrounding the image of the woman. One more circle, which includes images of fruits and vegetables, surrounds the circle of furniture. There are 24 small holes of various shapes around the edge of the coin.

Creative and Critical Thinking

■ Based on this coin, what do you think the main characteristics of this civilization were? How was it governed? What did the people do for a living? Would it have been a good place to live? Why or why not?

■ What are all the possible purposes for the holes around the perimeter of the coin?

■ Write a short story about an imaginary visit to the place and time represented by the coin.

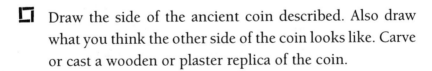

Artistic Design

❑ Draw the side of the ancient coin described. Also draw what you think the other side of the coin looks like. Carve or cast a wooden or plaster replica of the coin.

SOCIAL STUDIES:
IMAGINATIVE
ARCHAEOLOGY
AND
ANTHROPOLOGY

50
Complicated
Game

While traveling in a foreign country, you come across a large, oval grass field where some spectators are watching a ball game. The field has 12 holes in it, each three feet deep and two feet across. There are six big, strong players on each team. The players wear distinctive, colorful uniforms and protective equipment. Each player carries in one hand a 10-foot-long stick with a scoop on the end and holds a transparent plastic shield in the other hand. During play, three balls are used simultaneously. One ball is three inches in diameter and made of stone. Another is large, about three feet in diameter, and is made of a durable sponge-like material. The third is an ordinary soccer ball.

Creative and Critical Thinking

■ How would the players play this game? How would they score points, if indeed they score points at all?

■ What rules would the players follow? Write a list of rules for this game.

Artistic Design

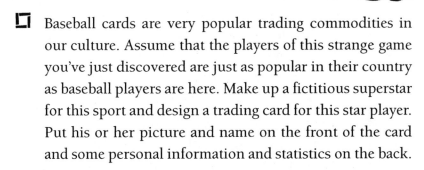

🗂 Baseball cards are very popular trading commodities in our culture. Assume that the players of this strange game you've just discovered are just as popular in their country as baseball players are here. Make up a fictitious superstar for this sport and design a trading card for this star player. Put his or her picture and name on the front of the card and some personal information and statistics on the back.

SOCIAL STUDIES:
IMAGINATIVE
ARCHAEOLOGY
AND
ANTHROPOLOGY

51

Emperor
of Ishbahar

You have just become the Emperor of Ishbahar, a small, land-locked, oil-rich nation in a large, remote desert. The eastern part of the country is sandy desert interrupted by scattered small oases. The western part is covered with rugged mountains. The only city in Ishbahar is in the foothills between the mountains and the desert. In spite of its oil resources, only a few people are wealthy: the friends of your father, who was the previous emperor. Most of the people in Ishbahar are poor, scratching out subsistence lives by herding animals and growing small amounts of crops in the oases.

Creative and Critical Thinking

- What would you like about being emperor?

- What unexpected problems might you face in your new role as emperor?

- What are some of the things you would do with your newfound wealth? What are the implications (both positive and negative) of this spending?

- It is unlikely but possible that technological development in the near future could make oil obsolete and relatively worthless. Knowing this, what plans, if any, will you make for the future?

Artistic Design

- Sketch a design of the $300-million palace the previous emperor built several years ago for himself, his family, and his friends. Show how you might change the palace now that you are in control.

SOCIAL STUDIES:
IMAGINATIVE
ARCHAEOLOGY
AND
ANTHROPOLOGY

52

The Merlakkans
of Doolmathon

The Merlakkan people from the planet Doolmathon are highly intelligent, friendly beings. They are extremely helpful and treat all creatures with kindness. They have developed highly advanced technology, but it is nothing like ours. Merlakkan society is quite egalitarian so everyone is roughly equal in status and material wealth. In fact, it is so egalitarian that there seem to be no leaders. Merlakkans look strange to us. They are about our size but shaped differently—very thin, with long legs and arms but short bodies. They also have long fingers, toes, and necks. Their skulls are large and bumpy, each with a ridge on top, starting between the eyes and ending at the back of the neck. They have long, flat noses, small mouths, and very large ears. They usually wear tight, one-piece suits made of a shiny, stretchable fabric.

Creative and Critical Thinking

■ Tell us something about Merlakkan technology. What does it help the Merlakkans accomplish? How does it work? What ideas might we borrow from the Merlakkans to improve our own technology?

■ The Merlakkans have seven rules for living printed on their suits. You have just managed to translate these rules into our language. Write out these rules so we can learn from them.

■ How could a society function with no leaders?

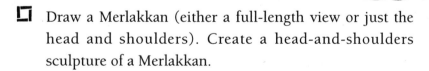

Artistic Design

⬜ Draw a Merlakkan (either a full-length view or just the head and shoulders). Create a head-and-shoulders sculpture of a Merlakkan.

SOCIAL STUDIES:
IMAGINATIVE
ARCHAEOLOGY
AND
ANTHROPOLOGY

53
Peculiar Sport

While traveling in a foreign land, you see a strange game being played in a stadium. Three teams consisting of eight players each are chasing after a large soft rubber ball on a large triangular grass field. An open-topped, barrel-shaped container sits in each corner of the field. There are wooden posts in the ground, distributed randomly throughout the field. The posts are numbered from one to 13, and each is a different color. The players wear running shoes, very strange uniforms, gloves, and protective masks. Players carry short, curved sticks. One player on each team occasionally blows a whistle while making hand signals. This seems to direct the players into group formations.

Creative and Critical Thinking

■ Imagine how the game is played and write a description. Include a list of rules for the sport.

■ Meet with a group of friends to consider your list of rules with the purpose of making improvements. If possible, collect the necessary equipment, set up a practice field, and try out the sport. Modify the rules again based on this experiment.

Artistic Design

⬚ Draw several players in action.

SOCIAL STUDIES:
IMAGINATIVE
ARCHAEOLOGY
AND
ANTHROPOLOGY

54
Ancient
Lamp

On an archaeological dig, you discover what must be the most beautiful lamp ever made. An artifact from an unknown ancient culture, the lamp has a solid gold base hammered into a beautiful, flowing design. The base has some hidden compartments covered with small, removable golden plates. There is no sign of what might have been stored in these compartments. A well-preserved fragment of red velvet is attached to the base with gold thread. Diamonds, sapphires, rubies, and emeralds are sewn into the velvet.

Creative and
Critical Thinking

■ What might have been kept in the compartments in the base of the lamp?

■ While translating an inscription engraved on the golden base, you discover that battles were often fought over this lamp. Why would armies go to war over it?

■ Based on your discoveries, speculate about the ancient culture that produced the lamp. How did the people live? What laws did they have? Who was in control?

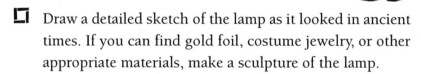

Artistic Design

⬚ Draw a detailed sketch of the lamp as it looked in ancient times. If you can find gold foil, costume jewelry, or other appropriate materials, make a sculpture of the lamp.

SOCIAL STUDIES:
IMAGINATIVE
ARCHAEOLOGY
AND
ANTHROPOLOGY

55
New Currency

Imagine that your local community becomes a separate nation with its own government and money. You are the leader of a government task force assigned the job of creating the new money for this young nation. Your new bills are called sporbots and the coins are called socculas. There are 25 socculas in a sporbot. Government leaders have decided that the sporbot should come in denominations of one, three, ten, 30, 100, and 1000. They have also decided not to put pictures of famous people on the bills. Instead, they want birds and animals that represent courage, strength, and other important characteristics that will inspire the people of this new nation.

Creative and Critical Thinking

■ Money seems to be very important to many people in today's world. How is this strong emphasis on money harmful or beneficial in our society?

■ Think of a way that your new nation could do without money. How would this work? Predict the outcome of this decision to do without money.

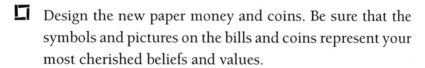

Artistic Design

🖸 Design the new paper money and coins. Be sure that the symbols and pictures on the bills and coins represent your most cherished beliefs and values.

SOCIAL STUDIES:
IMAGINATIVE
ARCHAEOLOGY
AND
ANTHROPOLOGY

56
Amazonian Vegetable

During a boat trip on the upper reaches of the Amazon River, you discover a strange plant unknown in the rest of the world. The plant is small and has a tough, thorn-covered skin. When disturbed, its brilliant flowers give off a fine airborne powder that irritates your skin and promotes violent coughing and sneezing. Nevertheless, eating the sweet-tasting pulp inside the plant provides tremendous bursts of energy that last for several hours. In discussions with indigenous people in the region, you discover that they have used this plant as a vegetable in their diet for centuries. They consider the plant sacred, and have hidden its value from outsiders until now.

We must view young people not as empty bottles to be filled but as candles to be lit.

—Robert H. Shaffer

Creative and Critical Thinking

■ What might the local people know about the plant that you don't yet know?

■ What are all the possible reasons why they might consider it sacred?

■ How might introduction of the vegetable into the modern world change our culture?

Artistic Design

☐ Draw a labeled diagram of the plant.

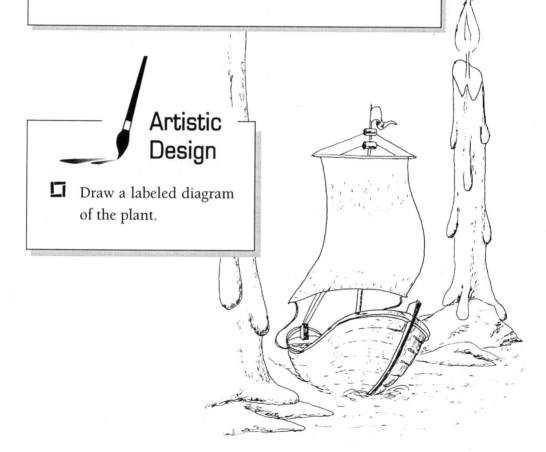

57

The Great Hall

In a European museum you come across a painting of an enormous room; in the painted room there is a large wooden table surrounded by 10 chairs. A medieval scholar you meet in the museum tells you that the painting shows the great hall of a palace in a small nation during the 13th century. Members of the government of this nation frequently met in the great hall. Unfortunately, little else is known about the history and government of this country, but looking carefully at the painting might provide some clues. One of the chairs at the table is larger than the rest. The back of this chair is so tall that it reaches the ceiling of the great hall (estimated to be about 50 feet high). The wood on the chair is ornately carved and studded with gold and silver ornaments. Three of the other chairs, placed near the large one, are not nearly as large and fancy, but they do have some decorative touches. Another three chairs, located further away from the biggest one, look like ordinary wooden kitchen chairs. The remaining three at the far end of the table are nothing more than small, three-legged wooden stools.

Creative and Critical Thinking

■ How do you think the government of this country operated? How were decisions made? What kind of decisions would these be?

■ Imagine that you took the painting off the wall, turned it around, and found an old document attached to the back. This document lists the eight rules that were used during meetings in the great hall. Write out these eight rules.

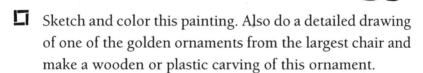

Artistic Design

⌐ Sketch and color this painting. Also do a detailed drawing of one of the golden ornaments from the largest chair and make a wooden or plastic carving of this ornament.

SOCIAL STUDIES:
IMAGINATIVE
ARCHAEOLOGY
AND
ANTHROPOLOGY

58
Ice Schooner

While you are traveling in the Arctic, a loud scraping noise causes the dogs in your sled team to stop in their tracks. Peering through the blowing snow, you make out a huge shape bearing down on your position. Suddenly, a large wooden ship goes sailing past you, skimming over the ice and snow at more than 40 miles per hour. It is traveling on three large skis: two on the back and one on the front. The ship has three tall masts with many sails. An unusual flag flies from the tallest mast. There are portholes along the sides of the ship.

Don't be afraid to take a big step if one is indicated. You can't cross a chasm in two small jumps.
—David Lloyd George

Creative and Critical Thinking

■ Where did this ship come from? Where is it going? What is its purpose?

■ Write a short story about its voyage.

■ Could such a vessel really travel across the Arctic? Why or why not?

Artistic Design

🔲 Draw the ship skimming over the snow and ice. Also sketch what you think the captain might look like.

SOCIAL STUDIES:
IMAGINATIVE
ARCHAEOLOGY
AND
ANTHROPOLOGY

59
Sword of Peace

As an archaeologist digging in a remote desert, you discover an ancient decorative sword that belonged to an empress who lived over 3,000 years ago. The sword has a long, broad, curved blade covered with decorative designs hammered into the silver metal. The hilt (handgrip) is covered with thin, woven wire of solid gold. A large red ruby is embedded in the end of the hilt.

Along with the sword, you discover some engraved stone tablets. After many days of hard analytic work, you are able to translate these tablets. They tell a story of a warlike period of history that ended after an empress came to power. With a symbolic sword, she was able to inspire the people of the region, both her subjects and their enemies, to set aside their differences and engage in peaceful trade for many years. You discover that the designs in the blade of the sword were the key to its effectiveness. The empress used the sword in ceremonial events, and the messages in the designs helped convince the people to strive for peace.

Creative and Critical Thinking

■ What were the messages in the designs on the blade of the sword?

■ Obviously, the empress must have been a great leader to make such a difference in the behavior of the people in these two civilizations. What personal characteristics do you think she possessed? Provide a detailed description of this empress.

Artistic Design

◩ Draw the sword. Also show a close-up view of one of the hammered designs in the blade.

SOCIAL STUDIES:
IMAGINATIVE
ARCHAEOLOGY
AND
ANTHROPOLOGY

60

Unknown
Artifact

As an archaeologist on a dig in southern Asia, you discover the remnants of a device once used in an ancient culture. The remnants include the following:

- two bronze hooks that look like large fish-hooks with dull points

- four pieces of wire (each five feet long)

- a flat, circular stone (four inches thick and two feet in diameter) with a hole in the middle and engravings around the perimeter

- eight bronze rings of eight different sizes ranging from three to 12 inches in diameter

There is some ancient writing at the site, which leads you to believe that the device was used for food production or preparation, but it doesn't specify how. The writing also doesn't tell you how the pieces of the device fit together.

Creative and Critical Thinking

■ What are some of the most likely ways that the pieces of this device fit together?

■ What are all the possible food-production or food-preparation purposes for which the device could have been used? Which of these purposes is most likely?

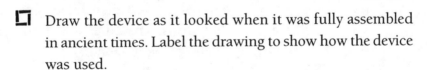

Artistic Design

▢ Draw the device as it looked when it was fully assembled in ancient times. Label the drawing to show how the device was used.

61
Ancient Freighter

During an offshore archaeological expedition in the Mediterranean Sea, you discover the remains of a sunken wooden ship and some of its ancient cargo. The ship appears to have been about 60 feet long and is about 3,000 years old. Some of the cargo remains include:

- fragments from two sandals (One sandal seems to have been very plain, made of wood and leather strips. The other was decorated with gold and precious stones.)

- three large, circular bronze plates, each decorated with an engraved portrait and unknown symbols (All three portraits appear to be of the same person but the symbols differ considerably from plate to plate.)

- fragments of very long oars

- a lion's tooth

- pottery fragments from many small bowls and jars, and large fragments from one huge jar, which was about six feet high and four feet wide

Creative and Critical Thinking

- What can these artifacts tell you about the civilization that produced the ship and its contents?

- Write a short story describing the last voyage of the ship. Tell the story from the captain's viewpoint.

Artistic Design

Draw a diagram of the ship as it was 3,000 years ago. Sketch some of the crew (and passengers if you think it carried any passengers). Show where the cargo was kept. Also, sketch one of the bronze plates.

PART IV

Creative

ARCHITECTURE

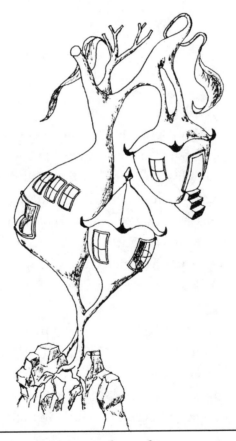

So few have imagination that there are ten thousand fiddlers to one composer.

—Charles F. Kettering

CREATIVE
ARCHITECTURE

62
The Tree Houses of Gwilf

A ll the people on the planet Gwilf live in tree houses. The trees on Gwilf grow to enormous sizes. Some are more than 2,500 feet high, taller than the tallest building on Earth, and the trunks are as thick as a football field is wide. The leaves on these trees grow large enough to cover the floor of a school classroom on Earth. The trees are deciduous, so the leaves fall in the cold season. Some trees have up to 100 houses in them. Some of the houses are carved right into the tree trunk while others are perched on, or hang from, the branches. The houses are connected to each other with staircases and rope ladders. The climate on Gwilf is hot and humid in summer, cool and dry in fall, cold with heavy snow in winter, and warm and rainy in spring.

Creative and Critical Thinking

◆ What would be the advantages and disadvantages of living in a tree-house village?

◆ The villages do not have electric power. How might electricity change the design of the houses and the villages?

◆ What problems and opportunities would the seasonal climate changes present for the villagers? How would the house builders plan for these changes?

Artistic Design

 Draw the design for three Gwilfian tree houses (one carved into a tree trunk, another perched on a branch, another suspended from a branch). For each house, draw an outside view and a cutaway view showing the inside. Also, create a wooden or cardboard sculpture of a house that hangs from a branch.

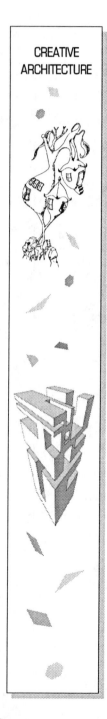

CREATIVE
ARCHITECTURE

63

The Deepest Home

The Mariana Trench in the western Pacific Ocean is the deepest known point in all the oceans of the world. At 36,198 feet below sea level the water pressure is tremendous. The strongest submarines in the navy would crumple like tin cans well before reaching that depth. Also, the water is cold, and it is very dark because light cannot penetrate the miles of water above. Scientists are becoming increasingly interested in the deep sea because strange life forms have been discovered. As part of a deep-sea research team, you are planning to investigate this deepest part of the ocean. Design a home in which you could safely live and carry out scientific research at the bottom of the Mariana Trench for a year's duration. The home must be self-sufficient, providing enough electric power, food, oxygen, and fresh water for your yearlong stay.

Creative and Critical Thinking

◆ What people or sources could you consult to help you with the design of this house? What design features would they recommend? Carry out some research to answer these questions.

◆ What would you like and dislike about your undersea work?

Artistic Design

 Draw a cutaway view of your deep-sea home. Label its important design features.

CREATIVE
ARCHITECTURE

64
Edible Home

On a visit to the planet Omneglor you discover that members of the local humanoid society make their homes in rapidly growing plants that reach heights of 60 feet. Each plant looks somewhat like a huge mushroom, so the top provides effective shelter from the frequent heavy rains. The outside layer of the plant is tough and leathery, but it can be stretched quite far with sufficient force. Long, transparent, hollow, tubelike vines hang from the top of each plant and stretch to the ground. The inside flesh of the shelter plant is soft and edible. It is very nutritious and tastes sweet. In order to construct their homes, the humanoids simply carve rooms out of this flesh. When the plant gets old, it stops growing and its flesh turns poisonous. The typical life span of a plant is fifteen years.

Creative and Critical Thinking

◆ What would be the advantages and disadvantages of living in one of these plants?

◆ Write a description of the living quarters carved into one of these plants.

Artistic Design

 Draw one of these plants after a family of humanoids has inhabited it.

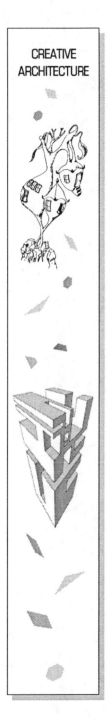

CREATIVE
ARCHITECTURE

65
Future Home

You travel 100 years into the future in a time machine. While traveling through a futuristic community, you see a For Sale sign on a house that looks nothing like houses from our time. Along with several prospective buyers, you decide to check out this home and take a tour with a real-estate agent. At first it seems that the home is just one big room with no internal walls. Much to your amazement, at a verbal command from the real-estate agent, soundproof walls slide up to the ceiling from narrow slots in the floor. These walls change from opaque to translucent to transparent at other verbal commands. After further inspection, you discover that this home has everything you can imagine for making life easier.

Creative and Critical Thinking

◆ Brainstorm a list of features this home could have to make life easier. Think about the conveniences we currently have and how they could be improved. Also think about conveniences we don't yet have that could be invented in the future.

◆ What would be the advantages of having the removable and changeable walls? Would there be any disadvantages?

◆ Is making life easier always a good thing? Think about the pros and cons of such a house. Write a short essay giving your views.

Artistic Design

 Sketch the inside of one of the rooms in the house. Label and describe all the appliances or conveniences it has that make life easier.

CREATIVE
ARCHITECTURE

66
Superbuilding

You are a famous architect who has been hired to design the tallest building in the world. The building must be able to withstand fires, strong winds, and floods. In addition, it must be self-sufficient, capable of providing its own power and water while enabling the residents to grow their own food. The building must have rapid vertical elevators along with moving hallways for horizontal travel on each floor. Finally, the building must have an atrium: an opening in the middle all the way from the first floor to the top. The atrium must be decorated with plants that vary from one level to the next. From balconies on each floor, a visitor should see tropical rain-forest plants in the lower levels of the atrium, desert plants at the middle levels, and northern evergreen trees near the top.

Creative and
Critical Thinking

◆ What would be the advantages and disadvantages of this building?

◆ Could you add any features that would make the building better?

Artistic Design

 Draw a cross-sectional, cutaway view of the building showing all of its important features.

CREATIVE
ARCHITECTURE

67

Escape-Proof Prison

There has been a rash of prison escapes in your community. Due to your reputation as a creative thinker, you have been recruited to serve on a task force that must solve the prison-escape problem. The plan you create must result in an escape-proof prison, but it has to be humane. It must involve no unnecessary or unusual punishment or cruelty. In addition, the plan cannot be too costly, or the taxpayers will complain. Keeping all these requirements in mind, plan this high-security prison.

Creative and Critical Thinking

♦ Some critics complain that prisons don't really rehabilitate prisoners. Instead of reducing criminal behavior, they actually promote aggression and teach inmates more effective methods of committing crimes. How could your prison positively change criminal behavior without cruelty?

♦ Are there better ways to solve the problem of crime in our society than by building better prisons? If so, describe how these methods might work.

Artistic Design

 Draw the design for the prison that you planned.

CREATIVE
ARCHITECTURE

68
Shipwrecked

After a vicious tropical storm, you find yourself shipwrecked alone on a small island in the South Pacific. The island is one mile long and a half-mile wide. Most of the island consists of bare rock and sand dunes. There are no trees: just small patches of tall grass in the sand. The only living things you see are seagulls on the beaches, some seaweed floating offshore, and some tropical fish swimming in a lagoon. Except during rare tropical storms, the weather is pleasant. The days are warm and sunny with occasional rain. The nights are cool and breezy.

Creative and Critical Thinking

◆ Make up a survival plan that will help you stay alive and reasonably comfortable for at least six months on the island.

◆ Make a list of ten things you hope to find when you open a large trunk that washes ashore from the shipwreck.

Artistic Design

 Sketch a shelter built from materials you find on the island. Include some close-up views that show the details of your construction methods.

CREATIVE ARCHITECTURE

69
Dream Home

Your inventions make you wealthy so you can afford a $5,000,000 dream home in the country. You design this home so it has everything you could ever want in it, including workshops and laboratories in which you can continue your inventing. The workshops include every tool and piece of equipment that an inventor would need. They also include storage bins for materials. Create the design for your mansion. Also plan the design for one of your invention workshops.

Good architecture lets nature in.

—I. M. Pei

Creative and Critical Thinking

◆ What are all the tools, pieces of equipment, and materials that an inventor would need?

◆ If you decide not to live in this house after all, what are some of its other possible uses?

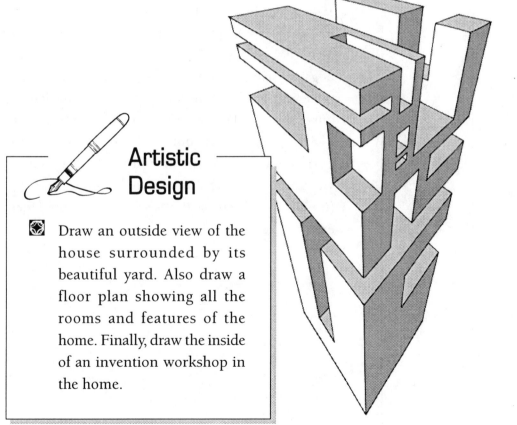

Artistic Design

◈ Draw an outside view of the house surrounded by its beautiful yard. Also draw a floor plan showing all the rooms and features of the home. Finally, draw the inside of an invention workshop in the home.

CREATIVE
ARCHITECTURE

70
Burrow Town

Imagine that there are other dimensions of reality, and we slipped into an alternate dimension. In this reality humans have no sophisticated technology, and common animals such as cats and dogs are five times our size. One way to hide from the least friendly of these animals would be to dig a burrow town much like the burrow communities built by prairie dogs in our familiar dimension. These burrows would consist of underground rooms of varying sizes interconnected by many narrow tunnels. Some of these tunnels would lead to hidden exits to the surface.

Creative and Critical Thinking

◆ What would you have to consider while building your underground community? Think about all the needs of a group of underground humans. Also think about what could go wrong underground and plan for these possibilities.

◆ Assume that you could bring five things along from our dimension into the new one to help you survive. What would those things be?

Artistic Design

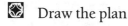 Draw the plan for your underground community. Label all of its rooms and its safety and protective features.

CREATIVE
ARCHITECTURE

71

Deep Viperion Cities

The planet Viperion is much like Earth except for a serious problem. Extreme solar radiation hits the planet once a year, making it impossible to stay on the surface for several months. The people of Viperion have created an effective solution to their problem. They have built tri-level cities that allow them to live on the surface when solar radiation is minimal, underwater when radiation is moderate, and deep underground when it is severe. The cities are built in the oceans. The top level of each city is on a floating island. The second, undersea, level consists of huge interconnected transparent globes. The underground level, deep below the ocean floor, consists of interconnected caverns structured much like anthills on Earth. The surface, underwater, and subterranean levels are connected by several huge elevators and some small ones, which allow for quick, efficient movement of large numbers of people from one level to the next.

Creative and Critical Thinking

◆ What would be the advantages and disadvantages of living in a Viperion city?

◆ The special attributes of Viperion cities create some unique employment opportunities that are unheard of on Earth. What job opportunities might you see listed in a Viperion newspaper?

◆ Write a short story about your yearlong visit to Viperion.

Artistic Design

 Draw the design plan for a typical Viperion city. Label and explain any important features.

Resources for Inventive Visual Thinking

The following is a list of resources relevant to the innovative visual and inventive thought processes emphasized in this book. The list is not comprehensive. Instead, it incorporates only a few sample resources that pertain to the insightful and expansive thinking that I hope the book encourages you to explore.

Visual Thought

The following resources provide insights about, and guidance for, visual thinking in creative work and invention.

Practical Strategies for Visual Thinking

Buzan and Margulies explore Mind Mapping, an outlining and brainstorming process in which the problem solver maps out a nonlinear, ever-expanding set of branches (subtopics) around a central topic, often incorporating graphic symbols to enhance the aesthetics and mnemonic (memory) power of the map. DeMille, Eberle, and Khatena provide strategies for guided visualization and other enhancements of visual imagination.

Buzan, T. 1993. *The Mind Map Book*. New York: Plume.
DeMille, R. 1973. *Put Your Mother on the Ceiling*. New York: Penguin.
Eberle, B. 1982. *Visual Thinking*. Buffalo, NY: DOK Publishers.
International Visual Literacy Association at www.ivla.org/index.htm (an interdisciplinary group dedicated to the discovery and dissemination of information about visual thinking; runs annual conferences, publishes literature on the topic, and networks through its website)
Khatena, J. 1984. *Imagery and Creative Imagination*. Buffalo, NY: Bearly.
Margulies, N., with N. Maal. 2002. *Mapping Inner Space: Learning and Teaching Visual Mapping*. 2nd ed. Tucson, Ariz.: Zephyr Press.

Visual Thinking as Thought Expansion

These books and articles show how excessive emphasis on verbal and symbolic processing (the norm in education) obscures the value of other thought processes, including visual thinking.

Armstrong, T. 2000. *Multiple Intelligences in the Classroom*. 2nd ed. Alexandria, Va.: ASCD.

Arnheim, R. 1993. "Learning by Looking and Thinking." *Educational Horizons* 71(2): 94–98.

Davis, J. 1993. "Why Sally Can Draw." *Educational Horizons* 71(2): 86–93.

Eisner, E. W. 1993. "The Education of Vision." *Educational Horizons* 71(2): 80–85.

———. 1994. *Cognition and Curriculum Reconsidered*. 2nd ed. New York: Teachers College Press.

Gardner, H. 1983. *Frames of Mind*. New York: Basic Books.

———. 1993. *Creating Minds*. New York: Basic Books.

———. 1993. *Multiple Intelligences: The Theory in Practice*. New York: Basic Books.

———. 1999. "A Multiplicity of Intelligences." *Scientific American* 9(4): 19–23.

Mathewson, J. H. 1999. "Visual-Spatial Thinking: An Aspect of Science Overlooked by Educators." *Science Education* 83(1): 33–54.

West, T. G. 1991. *In the Mind's Eye: Visual Thinkers, Gifted People with Learning Difficulties, Computer Images, and the Ironies of Creativity*. Buffalo, NY: Prometheus.

The Importance of Visual Thinking in Scientific Discovery

These writings highlight how visual thought contributes to scientific discovery in general and to the inspiring work of individual scientists.

Cheney, M. 1981. *Tesla: Man out of Time*. New York: Barnes & Noble.

Holton, G. 1996. "On the Art of Scientific Imagination." *Daedalus* 125: 183–208.

Miller, A. I. 1984. *Imagery in Scientific Thought: Creating 20th-Century Physics*. Cambridge, Mass.: MIT Press.

———. 1996. *Insights of Genius: Imagery and Creativity in Science and Art*. New York: Springer-Verlag.

Specific Visual Thought Processes

These authors explore the intricacies of visual thinking, from the mnemonic, synthesizing potential of imagery to the nuances of favored individual thought processes.

Daniels-McGhee, S., and G. A. Davis. 1994. "The Imagery-Creativity Connection." *The Journal of Creative Behavior* 28: 151–76.

John-Steiner, V. 1985. *Notebooks of the Mind: Explorations of Thinking.* New York: Harper & Row.

Creative, Inventive Thinking

These resources provide practical guidance for creative inventive thinking. Most include step-by-step guidelines for creative idea generation, problem solving, and invention.

Adams, J. L. 1986. *The Care and Feeding of Ideas: A Guide to Encouraging Creativity.* Reading, Mass.: Addison-Wesley.

Baer, J. 1997. *Creative Teachers: Creative Students.* Needham Heights, Mass.: Allyn & Bacon.

Costa, A. L., ed. 1992. *Developing Minds: A Resource Book for Teaching Thinking.* 2nd ed. Alexandria, Va.: ASCD.

Davis, G. A. 1998. *Creativity Is Forever.* 4th ed. Dubuque, Iowa: Kendall Hunt.

DeBono, E. 1970. *Lateral Thinking.* New York: Harper & Row.

———. 1985. *Six Thinking Hats.* London: Penguin.

Parnes, S. J. 1981. *The Magic of Your Mind.* Buffalo, NY: Creative Education Foundation.

Starko, A. J. 1995. *Creativity in the Classroom: Schools of Curious Delight.* New York: Longman.

Sternberg, R. J., and W. M. Williams. 1996. *How to Develop Student Creativity.* Alexandria, Va.: ASCD.

Treffinger, D., and S. Isaksen. 1992. *Creative Problem Solving: An Introduction.* Sarasota, Fla.: Center for Creative Learning.

United Inventors' Association at www.uiausa.com/index.htm (a nonprofit organization that provides inventors with educational services, leadership, and support, including helpful information on creative- and critical-thinking processes, advice on patent procedures, and opportunities to network with other innovators)

Von Oech, R. 1983. *A Whack on the Side of the Head.* New York: Warner.

———. 1986. *A Kick in the Seat of the Pants.* New York: Harper & Row.

About the Author

Don Ambrose, Ph.D., is a professor of graduate education and director of the Center for Innovative Instruction at Rider University in New Jersey. He works primarily with veteran educators moving into administration and aspiring teachers leaving other successful, established careers to join the profession. Prior to moving to a university setting in 1993, he spent 15 years in public education as a school administrator and teacher of science, social studies, art, and thinking skills. Dr. Ambrose's interest in K–12 education is ongoing; he frequently writes on topics such as school reform, giftedness, and creativity. He is also a talented artist—the fantastic drawings that appear in *Imagitronics* are the product of his own visual imagination.